From Home to School Literacy

Stories and Activities for Parents

Ann Gianola

Instructor, San Diego Community College District
San Diego, California

New Readers Press

From Home to School Literacy
ISBN 1-56420-490-1

Copyright © 2004 New Readers Press
New Readers Press
Division of ProLiteracy Worldwide
1320 Jamesville Avenue, Syracuse, New York 13210
www.newreaderspress.com

Printed in the United States of America
9 8 7 6 5 4 3 2

All proceeds from the sale of New Readers Press materials
support literacy programs in the United States and worldwide.

Acquisitions Editor: Paula L. Schlusberg
Content Editor: Terrie Lipke
Production Manager: Andrea Woodbury
Designer: Kimbrly Koennecke
Illustrations: James P. Wallace
Production Specialist: Jeffrey R. Smith
Cover Design: Kimbrly Koennecke

Contents

WITHDRAWN

Lesson 1: Don't Miss the Bus 4

Lesson 2: My Head Itches 8

Lesson 3: A New Girl at School 12

Lesson 4: Breakfast at School 16

Lesson 5: Read More at Home 20

Lesson 6: A Classroom Volunteer 24

Lesson 7: The Report Card 28

Lesson 8: Sign Up for Soccer 32

Lesson 9: Fighting at School 36

Lesson 10: He Can't Do Multiplication 40

Lesson 11: She Talks Too Much 44

Lesson 12: It's Bedtime 48

Lesson 13: Expensive Shoes 52

Lesson 14: Playground Safety 56

Lesson 15: Absent from School 60

Listening Exercise Prompts 64

Answer Key 67

Don't Miss the Bus

It is 6:45 A.M. Emily is in bed.
She feels tired.
Her father says, "Get up!"

Emily gets dressed and eats breakfast.
She brushes her teeth.
Then she combs her hair.

At 7:15 Emily runs to the bus.
She is late.
Emily yells, "Wait!"
The bus driver opens the door.
Emily is lucky.

Complete the story.

It is 6:45 A.M. Emily is in _____bed_____. She feels tired.
₁

Her _____ says, "Get up!"
₂

Emily gets dressed and eats _____. She brushes
₃

her _____. Then she combs her _____.
₄   ₅

At 7:15 Emily _____ to the bus. She is
₆

_____. Emily yells, "Wait!" The bus driver opens
₇

the _____. Emily is lucky.
₈

Check yes or no.

Yes **No**

✔   _____   **1.** Emily is in bed at 6:45 A.M.

_____   _____   **2.** Emily feels tired.

_____   _____   **3.** Her father says, "Wait!"

_____   _____   **4.** Emily eats dinner.

_____   _____   **5.** Emily combs her teeth.

_____   _____   **6.** Emily runs to the bus at 7:15.

_____   _____   **7.** Emily is late.

_____   _____   **8.** Emily yells, "Get up!"

_____   _____   **9.** The bus driver opens the door.

_____   _____   **10.** Emily is lucky.

Check yes or no about you.

Yes **No**

_____   _____   **1.** I am in bed at 6:45 A.M.

_____   _____   **2.** I feel tired in the morning.

_____   _____   **3.** I eat breakfast.

_____   _____   **4.** I take the bus to school.

Calling School

Read the dialog with a partner.

My daughter Emily is late today.
What is her last name?
Taylor.
How do you spell that?
T-A-Y-L-O-R.

Write the answers.

1. What is Emily's last name? _Taylor_

2. What is your last name? _____

3. How do you spell it? _____

What do they say?
Write the words below the picture.

✔ Wait!	I am tired.	Get up!

1. _Wait!_   **2.** _____   **3.** _____

My Head Itches

Ben is in class.

His head itches.

He can't think about schoolwork.

Ben goes to the nurse's office.

The nurse looks in Ben's hair.

She sees lice and nits.

Nits are lice eggs.

Ben has head lice. He needs to go home.

The nurse calls Ben's parents.

Later the nurse goes to Ben's class. She talks about head lice. She says, "Don't share hats and hairbrushes."

Complete the story.

Ben is in class. His head _____ . He can't think

1

about schoolwork.

Ben goes to the nurse's _____ . The nurse looks in

2

Ben's _____ . She sees _____ and

3   4

_____ . Nits are lice eggs. Ben has head lice. He needs

5

to go _____ . The nurse calls Ben's parents.

6

Later the _____ goes to Ben's class. She talks about

7

head lice. She says, "Don't share hats and _____ ."

8

Check yes or no.

Yes No

____ ____ **1.** Ben is at work.

____ ____ **2.** His head itches.

____ ____ **3.** Ben can think about schoolwork.

____ ____ **4.** The teacher looks in Ben's hair.

____ ____ **5.** The nurse sees lice and nits.

____ ____ **6.** Ben has head lice.

____ ____ **7.** Ben goes back to class.

____ ____ **8.** The nurse goes to Ben's class.

____ ____ **9.** She talks about head lice.

____ ____ **10.** She says, "Don't share hats and hairbrushes."

Check yes or no about you.

Yes No

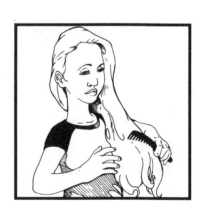

____ ____ **1.** I share my hairbrush.

____ ____ **2.** I share a slice of my orange.

____ ____ **3.** I share a glass of water.

____ ____ **4.** I share my pencils.

Calling School

Read the dialog with a partner.

My son can't go to school today.
Is he sick?
No, he has head lice.
What room is he in?
He is in room 7.
Thanks. I need to tell the nurse.

What shampoo do I buy?

Look at the shampoo label. Write the answers.

No Lice!
non-toxic lice shampoo
• Kills lice and their eggs
• Nit comb included
• For children and adults
$11.75
4 oz.

1. What is the name of the shampoo? _____

2. How much is it? _____

3. Is there a comb in the box? _____

4. Who can use the shampoo? _____

Lesson 2: My Head Itches   **11**

A New Girl at School

Carmen Cruz is from Mexico.

She is seven years old.

She speaks only Spanish.

It is her first day of school in the United States.

Carmen feels shy.

Everyone is speaking English.

Carmen doesn't understand the other children.

Carmen sits next to Angela.
Angela speaks Spanish too.
She is nice.
Carmen has a new friend.

Complete the story.

Carmen Cruz is _____ Mexico. She is
                        1

seven _____ old. She speaks only Spanish. It is
              2

her _____ day of school in the United States.
            3

Carmen feels _____. Everyone is speaking
                      4

_____. Carmen doesn't _____ the
          5   6

other children.

Carmen sits next to Angela. Angela speaks Spanish too.

She is _____. Carmen has a new _____.
                7   8

Check yes or no.

Yes **No**

____ ____   **1.** Carmen is from Mexico.

____ ____   **2.** She is six years old.

____ ____   **3.** Carmen speaks English.

____ ____   **4.** It is Carmen's first day of school in the United States.

____ ____   **5.** Everyone is speaking Spanish.

____ ____   **6.** Carmen understands the children.

____ ____   **7.** Carmen sits next to the teacher.

____ ____   **8.** Angela speaks Spanish.

____ ____   **9.** Angela is nice.

____ ____   **10.** Carmen has a new friend.

Check yes or no about you.

Yes **No**

____ ____   **1.** I am from Mexico.

____ ____   **2.** I speak Spanish.

____ ____   **3.** It is my first day of school in the United States.

____ ____   **4.** I have friends.

Meeting the Teacher

Read the dialog with a partner.

Hello. I'm Maria Cruz.
This is my daughter Carmen.
Nice to meet you. Hi, Carmen.
It is her first day of school in the
United States. She feels very shy.
Don't worry. We can help her.

Write the answers.

1. What is the girl's name? _____

2. How does she feel? _____

3. Can the teacher help? _____

Complete the sentences.

1. My daughter doesn't understand the other children.

She feels _____ shy _____ .

         shy   nice

2. It is my daughter's first day of school in the United States.

I need to _____ .

   sit next to the teacher   meet the teacher

Breakfast at School

Lamar is leaving for school.

His father is in the kitchen.

His father is holding a box of cereal.

He wants his son to eat.

Lamar doesn't have time.

Lamar is sitting on the bus.

He is not ready to study.

He is too hungry.

Now Lamar is eating breakfast at school.
He likes his pancakes and orange juice.
He feels better.
He is ready to study.

I feel better now.

Complete the story.

Lamar is _____ for school. His father is in

the _____. His father is holding a _____

of cereal. He wants his son to _____. Lamar doesn't

have time.

Lamar is _____ on the bus. He is not ready to

study. He is too _____.

Now Lamar is eating _____ at school. He likes

his pancakes and orange juice. He feels better. He is

ready to _____.

Check yes or no.

Yes   No

____ ____ **1.** Lamar is leaving for school.

____ ____ **2.** His father is in the living room.

____ ____ **3.** His father is holding pancakes and juice.

____ ____ **4.** Lamar has time to eat.

____ ____ **5.** Lamar is sitting in his father's car.

____ ____ **6.** Lamar is ready to study.

____ ____ **7.** He is too full.

____ ____ **8.** Lamar eats breakfast at school.

____ ____ **9.** He eats cereal and milk.

____ ____ **10.** Lamar is ready to study after breakfast.

Check yes or no about you.

Yes   No

____ ____ **1.** I like cereal.

____ ____ **2.** I have time for breakfast.

____ ____ **3.** I am hungry.

____ ____ **4.** I eat at school.

Reading the School Breakfast Menu

Read the dialog with a partner.

What is for breakfast tomorrow?
It is pancakes and orange juice.
Do you like that?
Yes. I want to eat at school.

What's for breakfast?

Look at the breakfast menu. Write the answers.

School Breakfast

Monday	orange juice, cereal, graham crackers, milk
Tuesday	applesauce, breakfast cheese pizza, milk
Wednesday	berry juice, French toast, syrup, milk
Thursday	chilled peaches, bagel with margarine, milk
Friday	orange juice, fruit yogurt, banana bread, milk

1. What day can you have French toast? _____

2. What day can you have fruit yogurt? _____

3. What days can you have milk? _____

_____

Read More at Home

It is 4:30 P.M.

Pedro's mother and father are at school.

They are talking to his teacher.

The teacher says that Pedro is a nice boy.

Pedro has one problem. It is reading.

It is difficult for him.

He is behind the other children.

The teacher says Pedro needs to read more at home.
He can go to the library too.
Reading is important.
Good students are also good readers.

Complete the story.

It is 4:30 P.M. Pedro's mother and father are at _____.
                                                        1

They are talking to his teacher. The _____ says that
            2

Pedro is a nice boy.

Pedro has one _____. It is _____. It is
        3   4

difficult for him. He is _____ the other children.
           5

The teacher says Pedro needs to read more at home. He

can go to the _____ too. Reading is _____.
        6   7

Good _____ are also good readers.
        8

Check yes or no.

Yes   No

____ ____   **1.** It is 4:00 P.M.

____ ____   **2.** Pedro's mother and father are at work.

____ ____   **3.** They are talking to Pedro.

____ ____   **4.** Pedro is a nice boy.

____ ____   **5.** Pedro has many problems.

____ ____   **6.** Reading is difficult for him.

____ ____   **7.** Pedro is behind the other children.

____ ____   **8.** Pedro needs to read more at school.

____ ____   **9.** He can go to the library.

____ ____   **10.** Good students are also good readers.

Check yes or no about you.

Yes   No

____ ____   **1.** I talk to my teacher.

____ ____   **2.** I need to read more at home.

____ ____   **3.** Reading is important.

____ ____   **4.** I go to the library.

Talking to the Teacher

Read the dialog with a partner.

How is my son doing in school?
He's having a problem in reading.
What can I do?
Your son needs to read more at home.

What will help Pedro?

Check the things that can help Pedro read more at home.

____ Books ____ Radio

____ TV ____ Electronic games

____ Magazines ____ Newspapers

Complete the sentences.

1. My son has one problem. It is _____.

the other children   reading

2. We can go to the _____ to get books.

library   home

A Classroom Volunteer

Mrs. Yong is a volunteer in her daughter's class.

She comes every Tuesday from 9:00 to 11:00 A.M.

This morning she is helping a group of students.

Mrs. Yong is holding a flash card.

The students are learning addition.

David doesn't understand an addition problem.

He raises his hand.

Mrs. Yong helps David understand.

Later Mrs. Yong is handing out papers to the class.
Mrs. Yong's daughter feels proud.
She is happy her mother is at school.

Complete the story.

Mrs. Yong is a _____ in her daughter's class. She

comes every _____ from 9:00 to 11:00 A.M. This morning

she is helping a _____ of students. Mrs. Yong is holding a

_____. The students are learning _____.

David doesn't _____ an addition problem. He raises

his _____. Mrs. Yong helps David understand.

Later Mrs. Yong is handing out papers to the class.

Mrs. Yong's daughter feels _____. She is happy her

mother is at school.

Check yes or no.

Yes   No

____ ____   **1.** Mrs. Yong is a volunteer.

____ ____   **2.** She is in her son's class.

____ ____   **3.** She comes every Friday from 9:00 to 11:00 A.M.

____ ____   **4.** Mrs. Yong is helping a group of students.

____ ____   **5.** They are learning subtraction.

____ ____   **6.** David understands an addition problem.

____ ____   **7.** He raises his head.

____ ____   **8.** Mrs. Yong helps David understand.

____ ____   **9.** Later Mrs. Yong is handing out books.

____ ____   **10.** Mrs. Yong's daughter feels proud.

Check yes or no about you.

Yes   No

____ ____   **1.** I volunteer at school.

____ ____   **2.** I raise my hand when I have a question.

____ ____   **3.** I understand addition.

____ ____   **4.** My child feels proud to see me at school.

Helping a Student

Read the dialog with a partner.

Do you have a question?

I don't understand this problem.

OK, what is seven plus one more?

One more than seven is eight.

You're right. Seven plus one is eight.

Check the children who need help.

1. ____   **2.** ____   **3.** ____   **4.** ____

Complete the sentences.

1. I _____ every Tuesday in my daughter's class.

    volunteer   learn addition

2. The boy _____ when he has a question.

    hands out papers   raises his hand

The Report Card

Roza is standing in front of her mailbox.
She is looking at the mail.
One letter is from her daughter's school.

Roza opens the envelope.
It is her daughter's report card.
She looks at the letters and numbers.
What do they mean?
She looks at the teacher's comments.
There are too many words. She doesn't understand them.

Roza goes inside her apartment.
She feels confused.
She needs help to understand her
daughter's report card.

What does this mean?

Complete the story.

Roza is standing in front of her _____. She is looking
1

at the mail. One _____ is from her daughter's school.
2

Roza opens the _____. It is her daughter's
3

_____. She looks at the letters and
4

numbers. What do they mean? She looks at the teacher's

_____. There are too many _____. She
5   6

doesn't understand them.

Roza goes _____ her apartment. She feels
7

_____. She needs help to understand her daughter's
8

report card.

Check yes or no.

Yes   No

____ ____   **1.** Roza is standing in front of her mailbox.

____ ____   **2.** She is looking at her daughter's school.

____ ____   **3.** One letter is from her son's school.

____ ____   **4.** Roza opens the envelope.

____ ____   **5.** It is Roza's report card.

____ ____   **6.** Roza looks at the letters and numbers.

____ ____   **7.** Roza looks at the teacher's comments.

____ ____   **8.** Roza understands everything.

____ ____   **9.** Roza feels proud.

____ ____   **10.** Roza needs help to understand the report card.

Check yes or no about you.

Yes   No

____ ____   **1.** My child's report card comes in the mail.

____ ____   **2.** I understand my child's report card.

____ ____   **3.** I call the school when I have a question.

____ ____   **4.** Sometimes I need a translator.

Calling the School Office

Read the dialog with a partner.

Can I help you?

Yes, I don't understand my daughter's report card.

Do you need a translator?

Yes, I need a Russian translator.

We have someone to help you.

Write the answers.

1. What doesn't Roza understand? _____

2. Who does Roza need to help her? _____

3. Can someone at school help Roza? _____

Complete the sentences.

1. I don't understand the teacher's comments. There are

    too many _____.

              teachers   words

2. I need _____ to understand my daughter's report card.

         an envelope   help

Sign Up for Soccer

Alfonso is sitting in his car.

He is picking up his daughter Marla after school.

Marla is very excited today.

She wants to play soccer with her friends.

Marla's friends are Kim and Margarita.

They play soccer in the neighborhood.

They wear uniforms.

Soccer is fun!

Alfonso doesn't know if Marla can play soccer.

He doesn't know the day, time, or place.

He doesn't know how much money it costs.

Alfonso needs to call Kim's parents.

We'll see.

Complete the story.

Alfonso is sitting in his car. He is picking up his _____ 1

Marla after school. Marla is very _____ 2 today. She wants

to play _____ 3 with her friends.

Marla's _____ 4 are Kim and Margarita. They play

soccer in the neighborhood. They wear _____ 5 . Soccer

is fun!

Alfonso doesn't know if Marla can play soccer. He doesn't

know the day, _____ 6 , or place. He doesn't know

how much _____ 7 it costs. Alfonso needs to call

Kim's parents.

Check yes or no.

Yes **No**

____ ____ **1.** Alfonso is sitting in his car.

____ ____ **2.** He is picking up his daughter after school.

____ ____ **3.** Marla is very sad.

____ ____ **4.** She wants to play softball with her friends.

____ ____ **5.** Marla's parents are Kim and Margarita.

____ ____ **6.** The children play soccer at school.

____ ____ **7.** Kim and Margarita wear uniforms.

____ ____ **8.** Soccer is fun.

____ ____ **9.** Alfonso knows how much money it costs.

____ ____ **10.** Alfonso needs to call Kim.

Check yes or no about you.

Yes **No**

____ ____ **1.** I like to play soccer.

____ ____ **2.** I like to watch soccer.

____ ____ **3.** My child plays a sport in the neighborhood.

____ ____ **4.** It costs money to play a sport in my neighborhood.

Calling Another Parent

Read the dialog with a partner.

Hello, Mrs. Shaw. This is Alfonso Luna, Marla's father.

Oh, hi, Alfonso. How are you?

Fine, thanks. What time is the soccer game this Saturday?

It's at 10:30.

Thank you.

Who wants to play soccer?

Look at the ad. Write the answers.

PLAY SOCCER! IT'S FUN!

Games for children every Saturday at La Mesa Youth Field

Sign up at the Mountain View Youth Center 1251 Ivy Street

Cost is $75 and includes uniform and team photo.

1. What day do children play soccer? _____

2. Where are the games? _____

3. How much does it cost to play soccer? _____

Fighting at School

Max comes home from school.
His face is dirty. His shirt is torn.
He is crying.
His mother asks, "What's wrong?"

There is a mean boy at school.
Fred hits and kicks.
He always wants to fight.
Max feels afraid at school.

Max's mother hugs him.
Then she calls the school principal.
She says that a boy is hitting her son.
Fred is in trouble. Fighting is bad.

I will call the principal.

Complete the story.

Max comes _____ from school. His _____
₁   ₂

is dirty. His shirt is torn. He is _____. His mother asks,
₃

"What's wrong?"

There is a _____ boy at school. Fred hits and
₄

_____. He always wants to _____.
₅   ₆

Max feels _____ at school.
₇

Max's mother hugs him. Then she calls the school

_____. She says that a boy is hitting her son.
₈

Fred is in trouble. Fighting is bad.

Check yes or no.

Yes   No

____ ____   **1.** Max's face is dirty.

____ ____   **2.** Max is crying.

____ ____   **3.** His mother asks, "How are you?"

____ ____   **4.** There is a nice boy at school.

____ ____   **5.** Fred hits and kicks.

____ ____   **6.** Max wants to fight.

____ ____   **7.** Max feels happy at school.

____ ____   **8.** Max's mother hugs him.

____ ____   **9.** Max's mother calls Fred.

____ ____   **10.** Fighting is bad.

Check yes or no about you.

Yes   No

____ ____   **1.** My child feels happy at school.

____ ____   **2.** I feel afraid at school.

____ ____   **3.** Sometimes I call the school principal.

____ ____   **4.** Fighting is bad.

Calling the Principal

Read the dialog with a partner.

This is Rose Johnson. I'm Max's mother.
How can I help you?
A boy at school is hitting my son.
Do you know his name?
Yes. His name is Fred.

Complete the sentences.

1. My son feels _____ at school.

        hungry   afraid

2. A mean boy at school is _____ my son.

        helping   hitting

3. I can call the school _____.

        principal   mother

4. _____ is bad.

        Fighting   Crying

He Can't Do Multiplication

I can't do this!

Pavel is doing his multiplication homework.

He doesn't like multiplication.

He counts on his fingers.

He is very slow.

He asks his father for help.

Pavel's father has an idea.

He goes to a school supply store.

He finds the flash cards.

He picks up the flash cards for multiplication.

Pavel and his father practice multiplication at home.
They sit at the table every evening.
Soon Pavel knows the answers quickly.
Now multiplication is fun and easy.

What is 12 times 3?

Complete the story.

Pavel is doing his multiplication _____. He doesn't
                                              1
like multiplication. He counts on his _____. He is very
                                                    2
slow. He asks his _____ for help.
                          3

Pavel's father has an idea. He goes to a school supply
_____. He finds the flash cards. He picks up the
          4
_____ for multiplication.
                              5

Pavel and his father _____ multiplication at home.
                                    6
They sit at the table every _____. Soon Pavel knows
                                        7
the answers quickly. Now _____ is fun and easy.
                                      8

Check yes or no.

Yes   No

____ ____   **1.** Pavel is doing his multiplication homework.

____ ____   **2.** He likes multiplication.

____ ____   **3.** He is very fast.

____ ____   **4.** Pavel asks his mother for help.

____ ____   **5.** Pavel's father goes to the supermarket.

____ ____   **6.** He finds the flash cards.

____ ____   **7.** He picks up the flash cards for addition.

____ ____   **8.** Pavel and his father practice multiplication at school.

____ ____   **9.** They sit at the table every evening.

____ ____   **10.** Now multiplication is fun and easy.

Check yes or no about you.

Yes   No

____ ____   **1.** I like doing homework.

____ ____   **2.** I like multiplication.

____ ____   **3.** Sometimes my child needs help with homework.

____ ____   **4.** I can help my child with homework.

Looking for Flash Cards

Read the dialog with a partner.

May I help you?

Yes. Do you carry flash cards?

Yes, we do.

Where are they?

They are in aisle 12, next to the pencils.

Write the answers.

1. What does the man need? _____

2. Where are the flash cards? _____

3. What are the flash cards next to? _____

Complete the sentences.

1. My child counts on his fingers. He _____.

    is very slow   knows the answer quickly

2. We _____ multiplication every evening.

    practice   pick up

She Talks Too Much

Justine is talking to her friends in class.

She is not talking about schoolwork.

She is talking about recess.

The teacher tells Justine to stop talking.

The teacher moves Justine to another seat.

Now she is sitting next to Albert.

Albert is working quietly.

Soon Justine is talking to Albert.

The teacher is angry.

The teacher writes a note to Justine's parents.
It says that Justine talks too much in class.
Justine gives the note to her parents.
They are upset.

Complete the story.

Justine is _____ to her friends in class. She is not

talking about _____. She is talking about recess.

The teacher tells Justine to _____ talking.

The teacher moves Justine to another _____. Now

she is sitting next to Albert. Albert is working _____.

Soon Justine is talking to Albert. The teacher is _____.

The teacher writes a _____ to Justine's parents. It says

that Justine talks too much in class. Justine gives the note

to her parents. They are _____.

Check yes or no.

Yes **No**

____ ____   **1.** Justine is doing her schoolwork.

____ ____   **2.** Justine is talking about recess.

____ ____   **3.** The teacher tells Albert to stop talking.

____ ____   **4.** The teacher moves Justine to another seat.

____ ____   **5.** Albert talks too much.

____ ____   **6.** The teacher is angry.

____ ____   **7.** The teacher writes a note to Albert.

____ ____   **8.** Justine takes the note to recess.

____ ____   **9.** The note says that Justine talks too much in class.

____ ____   **10.** Justine's parents are upset.

Check yes or no about you.

Yes **No**

____ ____   **1.** I talk to my friends in class.

____ ____   **2.** I am working quietly.

____ ____   **3.** My teacher is angry.

____ ____   **4.** I sometimes get a note from my child's teacher.

A Call from the Teacher

Read the dialog with a partner.

Good evening. This is Miss Campos.

I'm calling about Justine.

What is the problem?

She talks too much in class.

I am sorry. I need to speak to her.

Thank you.

Write the answers.

1. What is the teacher's name? _____

2. What is Justine's problem? _____

3. What does her mother say? _____

_____

Complete the sentences.

1. I get a note from my child's teacher. The teacher is angry.

   I am _____.

          quiet   upset

2. I tell my daughter to stop _____ in class.

          talking   working

It's Bedtime

It is 7:45 P.M. Mary is playing a game with her sister.
Her mother points to the clock.
She tells Mary to get ready for bed.
Mary goes to bed at 8:00 on school nights.
It's a rule.

Mary sits next to Daniel at school.
Daniel always feels tired in class.
He doesn't have a bedtime rule.
Daniel goes to bed very late on school nights.

Mary walks upstairs and
gets ready for bed.
She is in bed at 8:00.
Her bed feels comfortable.
Bedtime is a good rule.

Complete the story.

It is 7:45 P.M. Mary is playing a game with her sister. Her

mother points to the _____. She tells Mary
                              1

to _____ for bed. Mary goes to bed at
                      2

8:00 on _____ nights. It's a rule.
                3

Mary sits next to Daniel at school. Daniel always feels

_____ in class. He doesn't have a _____ rule.
        4   5

Daniel goes to bed very _____ on school nights.
                                  6

Mary walks upstairs and gets ready for bed. She is

in bed at 8:00. Her bed feels comfortable. Bedtime is

a good _____.
              7

Check yes or no.

Yes   No

____ ____   **1.** Mary is playing a game with her brother.

____ ____   **2.** Her mother points to the clock.

____ ____   **3.** She tells Mary to get ready for bed.

____ ____   **4.** Mary goes to bed at 7:45 on school nights.

____ ____   **5.** Mary sits next to her sister at school.

____ ____   **6.** Mary always feels tired in class.

____ ____   **7.** Daniel goes to bed at 8:00 on school nights.

____ ____   **8.** Daniel has a bedtime rule.

____ ____   **9.** Mary is in bed at 8:00.

____ ____   **10.** Bedtime is a good rule.

Check yes or no about you.

Yes   No

____ ____   **1.** I get ready for bed at 7:45.

____ ____   **2.** I go to bed at 10:00.

____ ____   **3.** I feel tired in class.

____ ____   **4.** My bed feels soft and comfortable.

Advice from the Teacher

Read the dialog with a partner.

You look tired, Daniel.

I feel tired.

What time do you go to bed?

I go to bed around 11:00.

That's too late. You need to go to bed earlier.

Write the answers.

1. How does Daniel feel? _____

2. What time does he go to bed? _____

3. What does he need to do? _____

Complete the sentences.

1. The boy doesn't have a bedtime rule.

   He feels _____ in class.

           tired   fine

2. Mary goes to bed at 8:00 on school nights.

   It's a _____ .

           game   rule

Expensive Shoes

Jamal and his mother are shopping at the shoe store.

There are many shoes.

Some are cheap, and some are very expensive.

Jamal likes the $100 shoes.

Jamal's mother wants to buy the $30 shoes.

She says they look almost the same as the $100 shoes.

Jamal says they are not the same.

Nobody at school wears the $30 shoes.

Jamal's mother is buying the $30 shoes.
She says $100 is too much money for shoes.
Jamal feels sad and angry.
He doesn't want the $30 shoes.

Complete the story.

Jamal and his mother are _____ at the shoe store.
1

There are many shoes. Some are cheap and some are very

_____.
2

Jamal likes the $100 shoes. Jamal's mother wants to

_____ the $30 shoes. She says they look almost
3

the _____ as the $100 shoes. Jamal says they are not
4

the same. _____ at school wears the $30 shoes.
5

Jamal's mother is buying the $30 _____. She says
6

$100 is too much _____ for shoes. Jamal feels sad and
7

angry. He doesn't want the $30 shoes.

Check yes or no.

Yes   No

____ ____   **1.** Jamal and his mother are at the shoe store.

____ ____   **2.** They are shopping for shoes.

____ ____   **3.** All of the shoes are expensive.

____ ____   **4.** Jamal's mother wants to buy the $100 shoes.

____ ____   **5.** Jamal likes the $100 shoes.

____ ____   **6.** Jamal says the $30 shoes and the $100 shoes look the same.

____ ____   **7.** Jamal is buying the $100 shoes.

____ ____   **8.** Jamal's mother wants to spend $100.

____ ____   **9.** Jamal feels sad and angry.

____ ____   **10.** Jamal wants the $30 shoes.

Check yes or no about you.

Yes   No

____ ____   **1.** I like shopping for shoes with my child.

____ ____   **2.** I like to buy cheap shoes.

____ ____   **3.** I like to buy expensive shoes.

____ ____   **4.** I think $100 is too much money for shoes.

At the Shoe Store

Read the dialog with a partner.

Excuse me. How much are these shoes?

They are only $30 on sale.

Are these $100 shoes on sale too?

No, sorry. Those are very popular. They never go on sale.

Write the answers.

1. How much are the shoes on sale? _____

2. Are the $100 shoes on sale too? _____

3. When do the $100 shoes go on sale? _____

Complete the sentences.

1. I don't want to spend $100. The $30 shoes look

almost the _____.

     sad   same

2. Nobody wears the $30 shoes at school. They are

not _____.

     popular   on sale

Playground Safety

It is recess time at school.

The children are playing outside.

The weather is cold today.

Renata isn't wearing a jacket.

Renata goes back to her class.

She puts on her jacket.

She runs outside.

Renata is running fast because she wants to play.

Then she falls down and hurts her knee.

Renata is crying.
The teacher asks, "Are you OK?"
Renata's knee hurts a lot.
She needs to go to the nurse's office.
Running on the playground is dangerous.

Complete the story.

It is _____ time at school. The children are playing

_____. The weather is _____ today. Renata

isn't wearing a _____.

Renata goes back to her class. She puts on her jacket.

She runs outside. Renata is _____ fast because she wants

to play. Then she falls down and _____ her knee.

Renata is _____. The teacher asks, "Are you OK?"

Renata's knee hurts a lot. She needs to go to the

nurse's office. Running on the playground is _____.

Check yes or no.

Yes No

____ ____   **1.** It is recess time at school.

____ ____   **2.** The children are playing inside.

____ ____   **3.** The weather is hot today.

____ ____   **4.** Renata is wearing a jacket.

____ ____   **5.** Renata puts on a sweater.

____ ____   **6.** Renata is running fast because she wants to play.

____ ____   **7.** She falls down and hurts her arm.

____ ____   **8.** Renata is crying.

____ ____   **9.** She needs to go back to class.

____ ____   **10.** Running on the playground is dangerous.

Check yes or no about you.

Yes No

____ ____   **1.** The weather is cold today.

____ ____   **2.** I am wearing a jacket.

____ ____   **3.** My knee hurts.

____ ____   **4.** There is a nurse's office at my child's school.

Help from a Teacher on the Playground

Read the dialog with a partner.

Are you OK?

No, it hurts!

What hurts?

My knee hurts a lot.

You need a bandage. Let me help you
to the nurse's office.

Write the answers.

1. Is Renata OK? _____

2. What hurts? _____

3. Where does she need to go? _____

Complete the sentences.

1. Renata falls down and hurts her _____.

    jacket   knee

2. Running on the playground is _____.

    crying   dangerous

Absent from School

Willie feels sick today. He can't go to school.

He is in bed and has a thermometer in his mouth.

Willie's temperature is 102 degrees.

He has a fever.

His father is sitting next to him.

He needs to stay home from work.

Willie's father calls the school.

He tells the attendance clerk that Willie is sick.

The clerk asks for Willie's last name.

She also asks for his grade and teacher's name.

Willie is in bed all day.
Later his mother feels his head.
Willie is still hot.
He can't go to school tomorrow.
He needs more rest.

No school tomorrow.

Complete the story.

Willie feels sick today. He can't go to school. He is

in bed and has a _____ in his mouth. Willie's
                            1

_____ is 102 degrees. He has a _____. His
          2   3

father is sitting next to him. He needs to _____
                                                          4

from work.

Willie's father calls the school. He tells the _____ clerk
                                                                5

that Willie is sick. The clerk asks for Willie's last name.

She also asks for his _____ and teacher's name.
                                    6

Willie is in bed all day. Later his mother feels his

_____. Willie is still hot. He can't go to school tomorrow.
          7

He needs more rest.

Check yes or no.

Yes   No

____   ____   **1.** Willie feels sick today.

____   ____   **2.** He has a thermometer in his mouth.

____   ____   **3.** His temperature is 99 degrees.

____   ____   **4.** Willie's father needs to stay home from school.

____   ____   **5.** Willie's father calls the doctor.

____   ____   **6.** Willie's father speaks to his teacher.

____   ____   **7.** The clerk asks for Willie's last name.

____   ____   **8.** Willie is in bed all day.

____   ____   **9.** Willie can go to school tomorrow.

____   ____   **10.** Willie needs more rest.

Check yes or no about you.

Yes   No

____   ____   **1.** I am sick today.

____   ____   **2.** I have a thermometer at home.

____   ____   **3.** I call the school when my child is sick.

____   ____   **4.** I stay home when my child is sick.

Too Sick to Go to School

Read the dialog with a partner.

My son, Willie, is sick today.
He has a fever.
What is his last name?
His last name is Shea. That is spelled S-H-E-A.
What grade is he in and who is his teacher, please?
He is in the fourth grade. His teacher is
Mrs. Grove.

Write the answers.

1. What's the matter with Willie? _____

2. What is Willie's last name? _____

3. Who is Willie's teacher? _____

Complete the sentences.

1. My son's temperature is 101 degrees. He has a _____.

        fever   father

2. My son is sick. I need to _____ home from work.

        sit   stay

Listening Exercise Prompts

Note to the teacher: Tell students to number a sheet of paper and then listen to the directions.

Lesson 1: Don't Miss the Bus
Write the time that you hear.

1. School starts at 8:00.
2. The bus comes at 7:15.
3. It is 7:30. Emily is late.
4. School ends at 2:45.
5. Emily gets up at 6:30.
6. We eat breakfast at 7:10.

Lesson 2: My Head Itches
Write the number that you hear.

1. My son is in room 7.
2. The class meets in room 5.
3. You need 2 bottles of shampoo.
4. The nurse is in room 10.
5. Please buy 3 new pencils.
6. Go to room 8 for your class.

Lesson 3: A New Girl at School
Write the number for the age that you hear.

1. Carmen is 7 years old.
2. Her brother is 8 years old.
3. My son is only 5 years old.
4. The boys are all 10 years old.
5. It's Olga's birthday. She is 3 today.
6. Her daughter is 9 years old.

Lesson 4: Breakfast at School
Write the day of the week that you hear.

1. There is cereal for breakfast on Monday.
2. On Friday we can have fruit yogurt.
3. They serve French toast on Wednesday.
4. Lamar eats at home on Tuesday.
5. What kind of fruit is there on Thursday?
6. On Tuesday there is applesauce.
7. On Thursday children like to eat bagels.

Lesson 5: Read More at Home
Write the time that you hear.

1. The meeting is at 4:30 P.M.
2. Please come to see me at 3:45.
3. School ends at 2:15.
4. We have dinner at 5:20.
5. The library opens at 12:30.
6. The class starts at 1:00.
7. The teacher can call you at 4:10.

Lesson 6: A Classroom Volunteer
Write the two times that you hear.

1. Mrs. Yong comes from 9:00 to 11:00.
2. School is from 8:00 to 2:45.
3. Class is from 10:15 to 11:30 A.M.
4. Your work shift is from 12:00 to 6:00.
5. The meeting is tomorrow from 3:30 to 5:15.
6. The movie starts at 7:30 and ends at 9:40.
7. The volunteers come every day from 1:00 to 2:30.

Write the day of the week you hear.

1. Mrs. Yong volunteers on Tuesday.
2. Can you come on Friday?
3. The game is on Saturday.
4. There is a test on Wednesday.
5. Is the meeting on Monday?
6. Your meeting is on Friday.
7. Music class meets on Thursday.

Lesson 7: The Report Card
Write the letter of the grade that you hear.

1. The citizenship grade is G. That means "Good."
2. Sammi's grade for Math is B.
3. Your daughter has an A in Science.

4. The Social Studies grade is C. You can work harder.

5. The grade for Reading is D. Your son needs to read more.

6. Eliza has an E in citizenship. That means "Excellent."

7. Tomas has a B in three classes. He is doing good work.

Lesson 8: Sign Up for Soccer
Write the prices that you hear.

1. Soccer costs $75.

2. Lunch costs $6.

3. Dance lessons are $10 for each class.

4. It costs $3 to use the pool.

5. I need $37 for a new backpack.

6. The total cost is $52.

Write the day and the time you hear.

1. The game is on Saturday at 11:00 A.M.

2. Class is on Wednesday at 10:30.

3. The team practices Friday at 3:15 P.M.

4. On Tuesday at 10:00, the students have a test.

5. The dance class meets on Monday at 9:45.

6. The children can play basketball on Sunday at 2:30.

Lesson 9: Fighting at School
Listen. Write Good or Bad.

1. A mean boy is hitting Max.

2. Sara is kicking her sister.

3. Rose is hugging her son.

4. The girls are fighting on the playground.

5. The boys are playing soccer.

6. The teacher is helping his students.

7. Roberto is reading a book about baseball.

Lesson 10: He Can't Do Multiplication
Write the numbers that you hear.

1. Where are the flash cards? They are in aisle 12.

2. Where are textbooks? They are in aisle 7.

3. Where can I find a stapler? Look in aisle 14.

4. Where do you have notebooks? They are in aisle 11.

5. Do you have any games? Yes, in aisle 8.

6. Are there backpacks here? Yes, look in aisle 6.

7. Where do you have pencils? They are in aisle 15.

Lesson 11: She Talks Too Much
Listen. Write Good or Bad.

1. Justine is talking to her friends in class.

2. Albert is working quietly at his desk.

3. Steven is playing soccer during recess.

4. Manny is doing a math problem on the board.

5. Frank is sleeping at his desk.

6. Richard is passing a note to his friend.

7. Laurie is reading her lesson in the science book.

Lesson 12: It's Bedtime
Write the time that you hear.

1. Mary goes to bed at 8:00.

2. She gets ready for bed at 7:45 P.M.

3. Daniel goes to bed at 11:30.

4. The TV show is over at 10:00 P.M.

5. Your meeting starts at 8:15.

6. The children need to be in bed by 9:30.

7. The movie starts at 7:20.

Lesson 13: Expensive Shoes
Write the price that you hear.

1. The shoes cost $30.
2. These fancy shoes cost $100.
3. Does the dress cost $45?
4. This red jacket costs $22.
5. I think $80 is too much money for jeans.
6. Some computers cost $700.
7. The new math books cost $10.

Lesson 14: Playground Safety
Listen. Write Good or Bad.

1. Renata is running on the playground.
2. It is cold. Cleo is wearing a jacket.
3. The bell rings. Eugene is walking back into the school.
4. It is cold. Albert is not wearing a hat.
5. It is recess time. The children are playing outside.
6. Jon pushes his brother on the playground.
7. It is raining. The children are playing outside.

Lesson 15: Absent from School
Write the temperature that you hear.

1. Willie is sick. His temperature is 102 degrees.
2. Sara's temperature is 100 degrees. She has a fever.
3. It's very cold today. The temperature is 22 degrees.
4. I'm hot. It's 95 degrees outside.
5. Wear your jacket. It's 44 degrees out.
6. The temperature today is 71. It's a nice day.
7. Sometimes the temperature in the desert is 115 degrees.

Answer Key

Lesson 1

Complete the story. (p. 5)

1. bed
2. father
3. breakfast
4. teeth
5. hair
6. runs
7. late
8. door

Check yes or no. (p. 6)

1. yes
2. yes
3. no
4. no
5. no
6. yes
7. yes
8. no
9. yes
10. yes

Write the answers. (p. 7)

1. Taylor

What do they say? (p. 7)

1. Wait!
2. Get up!
3. I am tired.

Lesson 2

Complete the story. (p. 9)

1. itches
2. office
3. hair
4. lice
5. nits
6. home
7. nurse
8. hairbrushes

Check yes or no. (p. 10)

1. no
2. yes
3. no
4. no
5. yes
6. yes
7. no
8. yes
9. yes
10. yes

What shampoo do I buy? (p. 11)

1. No Lice!
2. $11.75
3. yes
4. children and adults

Lesson 3

Complete the story. (p. 13)

1. from
2. years
3. first
4. shy
5. English
6. understand
7. nice
8. friend

Check yes or no. (p. 14)

1. yes
2. no
3. no
4. yes
5. no
6. no

7. no
8. yes
9. yes
10. yes

Write the answers. (p. 15)
1. Carmen
2. shy
3. yes

Complete the sentences. (p. 15)
1. shy
2. meet the teacher

Lesson 4

Complete the story. (p. 17)
1. leaving
2. kitchen
3. box
4. eat
5. sitting
6. hungry
7. breakfast
8. study

Check yes or no. (p. 18)
1. yes
2. no
3. no
4. no
5. no
6. no
7. no
8. yes
9. no
10. yes

What's for breakfast? (p. 19)
1. Wednesday
2. Friday
3. Monday, Tuesday, Wednesday, Thursday, Friday

Lesson 5

Complete the story. (p. 21)
1. school
2. teacher
3. problem
4. reading
5. behind
6. library
7. important
8. students

Check yes or no. (p. 22)
1. no
2. no
3. no
4. yes
5. no
6. yes
7. yes
8. no
9. yes
10. yes

What will help Pedro? (p. 23)
Check: Books, Magazines, Newspapers

Complete the sentences. (p. 23)
1. reading
2. library

Lesson 6

Complete the story. (p. 25)
1. volunteer
2. Tuesday
3. group
4. flash card
5. addition
6. understand
7. hand
8. proud

Check yes or no. (p. 26)
1. yes
2. no
3. no
4. yes
5. no
6. no
7. no
8. yes
9. no
10. yes

Check the children who need help. (p. 27)
Check: 1 and 4

Complete the sentences. (p. 27)
1. volunteer
2. raises his hand

Lesson 7

Complete the story. (p. 29)
1. mailbox
2. letter
3. envelope
4. report card
5. comments
6. words
7. inside
8. confused

Check yes or no. (p. 30)
1. yes
2. no
3. no
4. yes
5. no
6. yes
7. yes
8. no
9. no
10. yes

Write the answers. (p. 31)
1. her daughter's report card
2. a Russian translator
3. yes

Complete the sentences. (p. 31)
1. words
2. help

Lesson 8

Complete the story. (p. 33)
1. daughter
2. excited
3. soccer
4. friends
5. uniforms
6. time
7. money

Check yes or no. (p. 34)
1. yes
2. yes
3. no
4. no
5. no
6. no
7. yes
8. yes
9. no
10. no

Who wants to play soccer? (p. 35)
1. Saturday
2. La Mesa Youth Field
3. $75

Lesson 9

Complete the story. (p. 37)
1. home
2. face
3. crying

4. mean
5. kicks
6. fight
7. afraid
8. principal

Check yes or no. (p. 38)
1. yes
2. yes
3. no
4. no
5. yes
6. no
7. no
8. yes
9. no
10. yes

Complete the sentences. (p. 39)
1. afraid
2. hitting
3. principal
4. Fighting

Lesson 10

Complete the story. (p. 41)
1. homework
2. fingers
3. father
4. store
5. flash cards
6. practice
7. evening
8. multiplication

Check yes or no. (p. 42)
1. yes
2. no
3. no
4. no
5. no

6. yes
7. no
8. no
9. yes
10. yes

Write the answers. (p. 43)
1. flash cards
2. in aisle 12
3. the pencils

Complete the sentences. (p. 43)
1. is very slow
2. practice

Lesson 11

Complete the story. (p. 45)
1. talking
2. schoolwork
3. stop
4. seat
5. quietly
6. angry
7. note
8. upset

Check yes or no. (p. 46)
1. no
2. yes
3. no
4. yes
5. no
6. yes
7. no
8. no
9. yes
10. yes

Write the answers. (p. 47)
1. Miss Campos
2. She talks too much in class.
3. I am sorry. I need to speak to her.

70   Answer Key

Complete the sentences. (p. 47)
1. upset
2. talking

Lesson 12

Complete the story. (p. 49)
1. clock
2. get ready
3. school
4. tired
5. bedtime
6. late
7. rule

Check yes or no. (p. 50)
1. no
2. yes
3. yes
4. no
5. no
6. no
7. no
8. no
9. yes
10. yes

Write the answers. (p. 51)
1. tired
2. around 11:00
3. go to bed earlier

Complete the sentences. (p. 51)
1. tired
2. rule

Lesson 13

Complete the story. (p. 53)
1. shopping
2. expensive
3. buy
4. same

5. Nobody
6. shoes
7. money

Check yes or no. (p. 54)
1. yes
2. yes
3. no
4. no
5. yes
6. no
7. no
8. no
9. yes
10. no

Write the answers. (p. 55)
1. $30
2. no
3. never

Complete the sentences. (p. 55)
1. same
2. popular

Lesson 14

Complete the story. (p. 57)
1. recess
2. outside
3. cold
4. jacket
5. running
6. hurts
7. crying
8. dangerous

Check yes or no. (p. 58)
1. yes
2. no
3. no
4. no
5. no

6. yes
7. no
8. yes
9. no
10. yes

Write the answers. (p. 59)
1. no
2. her knee
3. to the nurse's office

Complete the sentences. (p. 59)
1. knee
2. dangerous

Lesson 15

Complete the story. (p. 61)
1. thermometer
2. temperature
3. fever
4. stay home
5. attendance
6. grade
7. head

Check yes or no. (p. 62)
1. yes
2. yes
3. no
4. no
5. no
6. no
7. yes
8. yes
9. no
10. yes

Write the answers. (p. 63)
1. He has a fever. *or* He is sick.
2. Shea
3. Mrs. Grove

Complete the sentences. (p. 63)
1. fever
2. stay